Fern Green

photographs by Deirdre Rooney

SUPER SMOOTHIES

hardie grant books

CONTENTS

Detox plans

INTRODUCTION

Today our bodies are exposed to toxins from when we get up in the morning to when we go to sleep at night. They come in the form of chemicals, pesticides, hormones and other pollutants, and can be found in our immediate surroundings from paint, skin creams, carpets, furniture and even tap water. Although our bodies have a natural built-in detoxifier which helps expel these toxins, there has been an increase of these substances, particularly in our food, which is putting a great burden on our health.

The build-up of toxins in our bodies can have lasting effects on our health, causing our immune systems to weaken. A lack of minerals makes the condition even worse and can result in a variety of symptoms including lack of energy, headaches, weight problems, allergies, mood swings and insomnia. To help our bodies detoxify efficiently we need to give our bodies some assistance in eliminating these harmful substances and a detox plan can help with this.

What is a smoothie detox?

A smoothie detox can give the body the time it needs to flush out the backlog of toxins. During a short detox the body is able to cleanse, purify and rebuild itself. A longer detox, of more than a few days, can result in deep cleansing at tissue level where accumulated toxins and waste have built up. Short fasts, lasting three to five days, are a wonderful way to rid the body of toxins and boost the system. They stimulate the whole metabolic process: excess weight falls off, your skin becomes clearer, your hair shines and your eyes brighten while the intestines are cleansed and organs release stored waste.

Who can smoothie detox?

Smoothie detoxing is, for the majority of us, completely harmless and anyone who wants better health and more energy can have a go. That said, those with chronic conditions, such as diabetes, heart disease, liver disease or cancer, as well as the elderly and pregnant women, should always consult their doctor first.

How often can we detox?

This depends on you and what other commitments you have in your life. Smoothie detoxes can vary, but one day a week is a good starting point.

What to drink in a detox?

The most powerful smoothies are those that are fruit-based with citrus. These are considered to be stronger intestinal cleansers than vegetable smoothies. However, a pure fruit detox may leave you feeling a bit off. In this book there is a mix of fruit and vegetable smoothies, which are recommended to drink throughout the day with plenty of filtered or bottled water and herbal teas.

WHAT EQUIPMENT DO I NEED?

Whether you are new to juicing or you are a regular smoothie maker, it's vital that you have the right equipment. Juicers are great if you are particularly keen on juices. They can create juice from most fruit and vegetables, but to make smoothies and nut milks where nuts, bananas and avocados are whizzed up, you will need a blender.

Using a blender

Blenders come in all shapes and sizes with many models now exploding onto the market. Do shop around to find one that suits your budget. You should look for one with a fast motor to whizz up all your ingredients to a fine pulp.

Making smoothies without a juicer

To make smoothies without a juicer, simply put all the ingredients into your blender, and blend them together. Tip the contents into a non-metallic sieve set over a jug, and, using a rubber spatula or wooden spoon, help the juice by slowly pushing it through the sieve. There is some washing-up to do with this method, but not as much as you would need to do with an electric juicer.

Useful equipment

- *blender*
- *plastic sieve*
- *large jug or bowl*
- *rubber spatula or wooden spoon*
- *saucepan*

HOW TO DESIGN YOUR OWN DETOX PLAN

Designing a detox plan can sometimes be difficult. Use the lists overleaf as a guide to help you choose what fruit and vegetables you need to use in your smoothies to help with different health issues.

What ingredients to buy?

When buying ingredients, try to buy organic fruit and vegetables as they are free of traces of artificial fertilisers and pesticides. They also contain higher levels of some vitamins, minerals and micronutrients and they are much better for the environment, soil fertility, and for us. Store fresh fruit and vegetables in a cool, dry place so that they last longer.

Getting ready for a detox

It is important to prepare mentally and to get into a positive frame of mind before you start. This will help you complete your detox happily. Try and set aside a day where you can relax and rest as much as possible as this will benefit your whole system. Perhaps have a massage or a sauna to help with the cleansing process, or just make sure you get a really good night's sleep.

Making sure that you have all the ingredients you need a day ahead is vital in preparation. Also try and eat lightly the day before, avoiding meat, fish, eggs, dairy and wheat. This is also useful when you have finished your detox to slowly bring your body back to regular meals. If you are a coffee addict, you may experience a caffeine withdrawal headache on a detox day. You can either choose to wean yourself off coffee during the week before, gradually cutting down a cup each day until you are at zero, or simply allow yourself one small cup of black coffee during the day to keep the headaches at bay.

Exercising during a detox

Any detox programme is greatly enhanced if you also take some light exercise such as yoga, walking or breathing exercises. A detox for three consecutive days is a commitment, so try not to organise a detox when you have a lot of other activities going on at the same time. Make sure your family and close friends know you are doing it, so they can support you and help make the process easier.

The first day

The first day is always the hardest. Your body needs time to adapt to going without meals, so you may feel a little hungry. Don't panic! The rewards are great, the hunger pangs will pass and you will have more energy and clarity of mind after detoxing than you might have believed possible.

How to make a detox smoothie

1

First, choose your leafy greens

cabbage, chard, kale, spinach, spring greens

2

Add your detox fruit & veg

see lists opposite

3

Add a boost

chia seed oil, cinnamon, ginger, maca, mint, nut butter, raw honey, vanilla

4

Add a liquid

coconut water, filtered water, nut milk

Top Fruit & Vegetables for a Detox

The list below is divided into different health issues to help you choose the best fruit and vegetables for that particular condition.

Skin health

Suffering from acne; skin needs a boost; anti-ageing

apple, avocado, broccoli, carrot, celery, fennel, grapefruit, kale, mango, melon, onion, orange, pumpkin, spinach, strawberries

Stress busting

Suffering from regular anxiety and stress

banana, broccoli, celery, kale, lemon, lettuce, lime, orange, peach, spinach, Swiss chard, tomato, watercress

Blood cleansing

Suffering from many ailments, including high levels of acidity in the body

avocado, beetroot, broccoli, cabbage, carrot, celery, grapes, ginger, kale, lemon, lettuce, orange, peach, pear, red peppers, spinach, tomato, watermelon

Digestion & constipation

Feeling sluggish; irregular bowel movements

apple, beetroot, blackberries, Brussels sprouts, carrot, cabbage, fennel, figs, grapes, kale, lettuce, orange, papaya, parsnip, peach, prune, pumpkin, watercress

Energy boosting

Slow metabolism; feeling tired

apple, apricot, banana, blueberries, cantaloupe, carrot, fennel, grapefruit, lemon, kale, mango, parsnip, peach, pear, peppers, orange, spinach, strawberries

The list below is separated into different colours to help you decide what to have in your smoothie on a daily basis.

Red

cherries, radishes, raspberries, red peppers, strawberries, tomato

- These foods contain lycopene.
- May protect cells, helping in the prevention of heart disease.
- Helps protect the skin from sun damage.
- May help to protect against certain cancers.

Orange & yellow

apricot, carrot, clementines, mango, nectarine, orange, papaya, peach, satsumas, sweet potato, tangerines

- These foods contain beta-carotene, which enhances your immune system.
- Convert to vitamin A in the body, essential for eyesight, immune function, skin and bone health.
- Contain hesperitin, which may lower cardiovascular risk.
- Contain beta-cryptoxanthin which helps prevent rheumatoid arthritis.

Purple

beetroot, blackberries, blackcurrants, blueberries, figs, plums

- These foods contain anthocyanidins which preventpain and inflammation.
- May support healthy blood pressure.
- Noted anti-ageing effects.

Green

apple, asparagus, avocado, broccoli, Brussels sprouts, cabbage, celery, courgette, cucumber, kale, kiwi, lettuce, melon, pear, spinach, spring greens, watercress

- These foods contain lutein and zeaxanthin, which helps protect the eyes from damage and reduces the risk of cataracts.
- Contain isothiocyanates, which have strong anti-cancerous properties.

White

parsnip

- Contains allicin, which increases the body's ability to fight infections.
- Strong antimicrobial, antifungal, antiparasitic and antiviral properties.

SPICY LEMON & LIME: THE CLEANSER SMOOTHIE

Makes: approximately 220 ml

YOU NEED

juice of ½ lemon • juice of ½ lime • pinch of cayenne pepper
1 thumb-sized piece of ginger • 1 teaspoon agave nectar

Add all the ingredients to the blender with 200 ml filtered water. Whizz until smooth, then pour into a plastic sieve over a jug or bowl. Help the smoothie through with a rubber spatula or wooden spoon.

Drink this smoothie every day of your detox. It will keep your metabolism on a high, boost immunity and alkalise your system.

M *Boosts metabolism* **B** *Blood building* **C** *Deep cleansing*

METABOLISM

Your metabolism runs your body, so boosting it can get your blood system pumping and your energy levels in to gear. We often become sluggish as we get older and feel like we need to slow down. Our metabolisms start to decrease, which leads to us burning fewer calories. If we don't change our diets, this can lead to weight gain. Exercising regularly, getting plenty of sleep and eating the right foods are all vital in helping you keep your metabolism burning at optimum speed. Try this smoothie plan to give your metabolism the kick it might need.

Top foods to help increase metabolism

Apples & pears
These delicious fruits are high in fibre, which will help you
feel fuller for longer.

Cayenne
Spicy peppers like cayenne can directly boost metabolism and
circulation. The compound capsaicin, present in cayenne, stimulates
the body's pain receptors, temporarily increasing blood circulation
and therefore your metabolic rate.

Oats
This is a wholegrain, containing complex carbohydrates, which speed
up metabolism by stabilising insulin levels. Oatmeal keeps your energy
on an even keel and helps prevent the body from storing extra fat.

How many days to detox?
This is a five-day detox plan, but if you
haven't detoxed before, I recommend
three days for your first try.

Preparation
Shop for all your ingredients two days
before. Stock up on extra lemons and
herbal teas, particularly green tea,
as there is evidence that this helps
speed up your metabolism. Make the
smoothies a day before to help you
keep to the plan.

Schedule
There are six smoothies to consume
each day. In the morning, start with
a very nutrient-dense smoothie,
breaking it up with smoothie 2, the
lemon and lime juice (see page
12), and end with a nut milk, which
will help to prevent you from being
hungry in the evening. You don't
need to drink your smoothie in one
go – you can slowly sip each one if you
prefer. I find a wide straw very helpful.

Daily plan:
Repeat this for every day of
your detox.

Smoothie 1: 8 a.m.
Smoothie 2: 11 a.m. (see page 12)
Smoothie 3: 1 p.m.
Smoothie 4: 3 p.m.
Smoothie 5: 5 p.m.
Smoothie 6: 7:30 p.m.

You don't need to stick to these times,
but allow a two-hour gap before bed.
Continue to drink lots of water;
I recommend 6–8 glasses a day.

OATY NANA: SMOOTHIE 1

Makes: approximately 300 ml

YOU NEED

2 tablespoons oatbran • 1 banana, peeled • 200 g natural yoghurt
1 tablespoon coconut oil • 1 Medjool date, stoned

Add all the ingredients to the blender with 100 ml filtered water.
Whizz until smooth.

This helps to keep your blood sugar levels on an even keel.

C *Lowers cholesterol* D *Aids digestion* R *Revitalising*

KALE CARE: SMOOTHIE 3

Makes: approximately 300 ml

YOU NEED
3 handfuls of kale • 2 pears, cored • 1 lime, peeled • handful of green grapes

Add all the ingredients to the blender with 150 ml filtered water. Whizz until smooth then pour into a plastic sieve set over a jug or bowl. Help the smoothie through with a rubber spatula or wooden spoon.

Full of vitamin K, which helps strengthen our bones, prevents calcium build-up in our tissues and improves our nervous system.

B *Blood building*   D *Aids digestion*   M *Mineral rich*

LIME ZEST: SMOOTHIE 4

Makes: approximately 250 ml

YOU NEED

2 pears, cored • handful of baby spinach

5 broccoli florets • 1 lime, ½ zested, then peeled

Add all the ingredients to the blender with 200 ml filtered water. Whizz until smooth, then pour into a plastic sieve set over a jug or bowl. Help the smoothie through with a rubber spatula or wooden spoon.

This is full of flavonoids which help to rejuvenate the skin.

B *Blood purifying*   **A** *Anti-inflammatory*   **B** *Lowers blood pressure*

CARROT FRESH: SMOOTHIE 5

Makes: approximately 400 ml

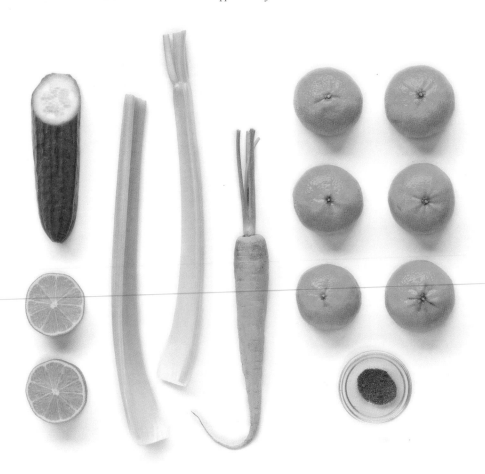

YOU NEED

1 carrot • pinch of cayenne pepper • 6 clementines, peeled
1 lime, peeled • 2 celery sticks • ¼ cucumber

Add all the ingredients to the blender with 100 ml filtered water. Whizz until
smooth then pour into a plastic sieve set over a jug or bowl. Help the smoothie
through with a rubber spatula or wooden spoon.

This is good for boosting circulation and energising your heart.

V *Vitamin rich*   M *Boosts metabolism*   A *Anti-inflammatory*

VANILLA NUT MILK CHAI: SMOOTHIE 6

Makes: approximately 300 ml

YOU NEED

75 g cashew nuts • 2 drops of vanilla extract • 1 tablespoon coconut oil
1 teaspoon raw cacao nibs • 2 Medjool dates, stoned • 1 chai tea bag

Add all the ingredients, apart from the tea bag, to the blender with 300 ml filtered water. Whizz until smooth; pour into a plastic sieve set over a jug or bowl. Help the milk through with a rubber spatula or wooden spoon. Pour it into a saucepan and add the chai tea bag. Warm gently over a low heat for 3–4 minutes.

This milk contains phosphorus, which provides energy and helps strengthen your teeth and bones.

C *Calming* **H** *Healing* **I** *Fights infection*

CLEAR SKIN

Everyone's skin battles daily with exposure to toxins from pollution, sun damage and chemicals. These can all contribute to your skin's health and deterioration, leading to premature wrinkles. As your skin is your first line of defence against the environment, it's important to keep it supple and strong. Skin problems range from eczema and psoriasis to acne and wrinkles. These all need a little bit of help from the inside. No one wants dry, flaky skin or excess oil production, which can cause breakouts and thinning of the skin.

Top fruit & vegetables to help with skin health

Apples
As well as being full of phytonutrients, apples contain enzymes that help break down carbohydrates. These help to regulate blood sugar levels, which is important in skin health, as spikes in blood sugar can damage collagen.

Cucumber
Full of minerals and B vitamins, cucumber is brilliant for hydrating the skin as it is 95% water and contains important electrolytes.

Fennel
A great source of vitamin C, which helps regenerate and repair your cells. Supporting the process of collagen formation, fennel also contains a particular phytonutrient that reduces inflammation and contains natural antibacterial properties, which balances the bacteria in your gut and promotes detoxification.

How many days to detox?
If you have never detoxed before, then you may want to start with a three-day detox. If you regularly drink green smoothies, have detoxed before, or eat a lot of raw food, then you can extend this to a five-day detox.

Preparation
Shop for all your ingredients two days before. Stock up on extra lemons and herbal teas to help with your detox. Make the smoothies and juices a day before to help you keep to the plan.

Schedule
There are six smoothies to consume each day. In the morning, start with a very nutrient-dense smoothie, breaking it up with smoothie 2, the lemon and lime juice (see page 12),

and ending with a nut milk, which will help prevent you being hungry in the evening. You don't need to drink your smoothie in one go – you can slowly sip each one if you prefer. I find a wide straw very helpful.

Daily plan:
Repeat this for every day of your detox.

Smoothie 1: 8 a.m.
Smoothie 2: 11 a.m. (see page 12)
Smoothie 3: 1 p.m.
Smoothie 4: 3 p.m.
Smoothie 5: 5 p.m.
Smoothie 6: 7:30 p.m.

You don't need to stick to these times, but allow a two-hour gap before you go to bed. Continue to drink lots of water; I recommend 6–8 glasses a day.

APPLE LUSH: SMOOTHIE 1

Makes: approximately 300 ml

YOU NEED

½ green apple, cored • ½ red apple, cored • 1 celery stick
½ yellow pepper • handful of spinach • ½ fennel bulb
handful of kale • ½ lemon, peeled • 1 thumb-sized piece of ginger • ¼ cucumber

---

Add all the ingredients to the blender with 100 ml filtered water. Whizz until smooth then pour into a plastic sieve set over a jug or bowl. Help the smoothie through with a rubber spatula or wooden spoon.

Full of vitamins including A, C, B and B6, this smoothie also contains a high amount of folate, which helps your body to make DNA.

B *Stabilises blood sugar*　**A** *Anti-inflammatory*　**H** *Hydrating*

PINEAPPLE BOOST: SMOOTHIE 3

Makes: approximately 300 ml

YOU NEED
1 orange, peeled • ½ fennel bulb • 50 ml aloe vera juice
½ pineapple, peeled and cut into chunks • 10 mint leaves • 2 handfuls of spinach

---

Add the ingredients to the blender. Whizz until smooth; pour into a plastic sieve set
over a jug or bowl. Help the smoothie through with a spatula or wooden spoon.

This is high in vitamin C, which is required for collagen synthesis. Collagen is the main structural protein required for maintaining blood vessels, skin and bones.

Ⓐ *Anti-inflammatory* Ⓜ *Mineral rich* Ⓓ *Aids digestion*

THAI CUCUMBER: SMOOTHIE 4

Makes: approximately 300 ml

YOU NEED

¼ cucumber • ½ cantaloupe (about 150 g), peeled

1 lemongrass stalk • 2 handfuls of kale • 100 ml coconut water

Add the ingredients to the blender. Whizz until smooth; pour into a plastic sieve set over a jug or bowl. Help the smoothie through with a spatula or wooden spoon.

This smoothie is high in vitamin A, which is important for healthy teeth, skin, bones and mucus membranes. It also helps with eyesight.

H *Healing* **A** *Anti-inflammatory* **D** *Detoxifying*

GREEN GLOW: SMOOTHIE 5

Makes: approximately 300 ml

YOU NEED

3 broccoli florets • ½ fennel bulb • 1 apple, cored • ¼ cucumber • 5 coriander sprigs

Add all the ingredients to the blender with 100 ml filtered water. Whizz until
smooth then pour into a plastic sieve set over a jug or bowl. Help the smoothie
through with a rubber spatula or wooden spoon.

This is full of nutrients that help fight diseases.

H *Hydrating* **P** *Purifying* **M** *Mineral rich*

TURMERIC ALMOND MILK: SMOOTHIE 6

Makes: approximately 320 ml

YOU NEED

100 g almonds • ½ teaspoon ground turmeric • 2 dates, stoned • pinch of salt

---

Add all the ingredients to the blender with 300 ml filtered water. Whizz until smooth then pour into a plastic sieve set over a jug or bowl. Help the milk through with a rubber spatula or wooden spoon.

This is a high-protein milk, which encourages alkalinity. It also helps to regulate blood sugar and staves off hunger.

S *Improves skin* **I** *Fights infection* **D** *Detoxifying*

ENERGY BOOSTER

Frequent exercise has an immediate effect on mood and heart health. We also know that it can be a great boost to our energy levels. On the other hand, if we are not eating the right foods or fuelling up on carbohydrates, it can often have an adverse effect on our energy levels. Slow-release carbohydrates like vegetables and whole grains such as quinoa, spelt and brown rice are great energy-boosting options. Protein is also necessary for training and recovery as it helps restore and repair muscle tissue. Good sources are eggs, legumes, nuts and seeds. This detox plan has been created for when you are feeling a little lacklustre and need an energy boost, as well as supporting your body if you are exercising regularly.

Top fruit & vegetables to help boost energy

Bananas
These are a great source of antioxidants and healthy carbohydrates. Bananas are low in fibre, making them easy to digest.

Grapefruit
Packed with vitamin C, which plays a role in helping your body form amino acids, precursors to chemicals that regulate your energy levels.

Spinach
This is great for boosting your body with iron. If you don't consume enough iron, your body doesn't get enough oxygen, so iron deficiency can be a common cause of fatigue.

Sweet potato
This starchy vegetable contains vitamin C and slow-releasing carbohydrates that provide you with long lasting energy.

How many days to detox?
This is a three-day detox plan.

Preparation
Shop for all your ingredients two days before. Stock up on extra lemons and herbal teas to help with your detox. Make the smoothies and juices a day before to help you keep to the plan.

Schedule
There are six smoothies to consume each day. In the morning start with a very nutrient-dense smoothie, breaking it up with smoothie 2, the lemon and lime juice (see page 12), and ending with a nut milk, which will help prevent you from being hungry in the evening.

You don't need to drink your smoothie in one go – you can slowly sip each one if you prefer. I find a wide straw to be very helpful.

Daily plan:
Repeat this for every day of your detox.

Smoothie 1: 8 a.m.
Smoothie 2: 11 a.m. (see page 12)
Smoothie 3: 1 p.m.
Smoothie 4: 3 p.m.
Smoothie 5: 5 p.m.
Smoothie 6: 7:30 p.m.

You don't need to stick to these times, but allow a two-hour gap before you go to bed. Continue to drink lots of water; I recommend 6–8 glasses a day.

SWEET POTATO: SMOOTHIE 1

Makes: approximately 300 ml

YOU NEED

1 medium sweet potato, peeled and chopped into small chunks • 2 handfuls of kale
handful of spinach • 2 peaches, stoned • 2 mint sprigs • 1 lime, peeled

---

Add all the ingredients to the blender with 200 ml filtered water. Whizz until
smooth then pour into a plastic sieve set over a jug or bowl. Help the smoothie
through with a rubber spatula or wooden spoon.

Contains high amounts of vitamin D, which plays an important role in our energy levels, moods and helps to build healthy bones, heart, nerves, skin and teeth.

E *Energising*　**M** *Mineral rich*　**D** *Aids digestion*

BANANA BOOST: SMOOTHIE 3

Makes: approximately 250 ml

YOU NEED

1 banana, peeled • 1 tablespoon peanut butter • 250 ml coconut water

---

Add all the ingredients to the blender and whizz until smooth.

This is high in potassium and vitamin B6, which is great for preventing high blood pressure.

D *Aids digestion* **H** *Hydrating* **E** *Energising*

GRAPEFRUIT GROWER: SMOOTHIE 4

Makes: approximately 250 ml

YOU NEED

1 medium carrot • 1 handful of spinach • 1 handful of kale
1 orange, peeled • 1 grapefruit, peeled

Add all the ingredients to the blender with 100 ml filtered water. Whizz until smooth then pour into a plastic sieve set over a jug or bowl. Help the smoothie through with a rubber spatula or wooden spoon.

This helps to curb hunger and is also high in vitamin C and betacarotene.

V *Vitamin rich* **A** *Alkalising* **R** *Refreshing*

REFRESHING BEETROOT: SMOOTHIE 5

Makes: approximately 300 ml

YOU NEED

3 beetroots, chopped • handful of baby spinach • 2 handfuls of blueberries
¼ cucumber

Add all the ingredients to the blender with 150 ml filtered water. Whizz until
smooth then pour into a plastic sieve set over a jug or bowl. Help the smoothie
through with a rubber spatula or wooden spoon.

Helps to boost your stamina and enables muscles to work more efficiently, reducing blood pressure.

E *Energising* **B** *Blood building* **S** *Strengthening*

SPICED SWEET POTATO MILK: SMOOTHIE 6

Makes: approximately 300 ml

YOU NEED

75 g blanched almonds • 1 medium sweet potato, peeled and chopped • ½ teaspoon
ground cinnamon • pinch of ground cloves • 1 thumb-sized piece of ginger
2 Medjool dates • 1 teaspoon honey • pinch of salt

Add all the ingredients to the blender with 300 ml filtered water. Whizz until
smooth then pour into a plastic sieve set over a jug or bowl. Help the milk through
with a rubber spatula or wooden spoon. Feel free to warm it up if you would prefer
by slowly heating it in a saucepan for 3–4 minutes.

Helps to regulate your blood sugar levels and keeps hunger at bay.

R *Revitalising* **BP** *Lowers blood pressure* **C** *Calming*

DIGESTION

*The gut, otherwise known as your second brain,
is an important part of your body to keep healthy.
Undigested material and debris need to continue
moving towards the large intestine where water is
absorbed and faecal matter is formed. If you are a
healthy eater, getting rid of this matter will be easy, but
if your diet is high in animal products and processed
foods, it might be a painful part of your week! The
large intestine is the major detoxification organ in the
body, therefore it is vital to keep it clean and toned so it
can absorb nutrients properly. Eating a mostly plant-
based, whole-food diet, and drinking green smoothies,
will keep nasty toxins away and repair damage
to cell tissue from free radicals.*

Top fruit & vegetables to help with digestion

Apples
These contain a natural laxative called sorbitol, which holds on to
water as it makes its way through the gut, drawing it into the large
intestine. This increases the moisture content, which promotes
regular bowel movements. Sorbitol can also be found in
prunes, peaches and pears.

Carrots
A great food to support the liver. Carrots encourage bile production,
which helps with constipation by binding bile acids. This promotes
peristalsis and the movement of waste through the intestine.

Papayas
Rich in enzymes that help break down dietary proteins in the stomach
and intestines, papaya regulates the digestive system and supports
peristalsis, which promotes regular bowel movements.

How many days to detox?
This is a five-day detox plan, but if you
haven't detoxed before, I recommend
three days for your first try.

Preparation
Shop for all your ingredients two days
before. Stock up on extra lemons
and herbal teas, particularly mint,
nettle and fennel, as these help with
digestion. Make the smoothies and
juices a day before to help you keep
to the plan.

Schedule
There are six smoothies to consume
each day. In the morning start with
a very nutrient-dense smoothie,
breaking it up with smoothie 2, the
lemon and lime juice (see page 12),
and end with a nut milk, which will
help prevent you from being hungry
in the evening. You don't need to
drink your smoothie in one go – you
can slowly sip each one if you prefer. I
find a wide straw very helpful.

Daily plan:
Repeat this for every day of
your detox.

Smoothie 1: 8 a.m.
Smoothie 2: 11 a.m. (see page 12)
Smoothie 3: 1 p.m.
Smoothie 4: 3 p.m.
Smoothie 5: 5 p.m.
Smoothie 6: 7:30 p.m.

You don't need to stick to these times,
but allow a two-hour gap before bed.
Continue to drink lots of water;
I recommend 6–8 glasses a day.

DIGESTIVO: SMOOTHIE 1

Makes: approximately 300 ml

YOU NEED

1 papaya, peeled and deseeded • 2 handfuls of kale
1 green apple, cored • 1 red apple, cored • 1 carrot

Add all the ingredients to the blender with 200 ml filtered water. Whizz until
smooth then pour into a plastic sieve set over a jug or bowl. Help the smoothie
through with a rubber spatula or wooden spoon.

This is great at breaking down proteins, which helps improve digestion.

D *Aids digestion* **L** *Cleanses liver* **H** *Hydrating*

PEACHY CARROTS: SMOOTHIE 3

Makes: approximately 300 ml

YOU NEED

2 peaches, stoned • handful of spinach • 2 medium carrots • ¼ cucumber

---

Add all the ingredients to the blender with 200 ml filtered water. Whizz until smooth then pour into a plastic sieve set over a jug or bowl. Help the smoothie through with a rubber spatula or wooden spoon.

Full of vitamins and minerals as well as antioxidants and fibre, this is a great all-rounder.

L *Cleanses liver* **C** *Lowers cholesterol* **V** *Vitamin rich*

BERRY BUZZ: SMOOTHIE 4

Makes: approximately 300 ml

YOU NEED

handful of kale • ½ cos lettuce • 10 strawberries, stalks removed
1 kiwi, peeled • 1 lime, peeled

Add all the ingredients to the blender with 150 ml filtered water. Whizz until smooth then pour into a plastic sieve set over a jug or bowl. Help the smoothie through with a rubber spatula or wooden spoon.

This smoothie is a rich source of vitamin C and fibre
and also helps to lower cholesterol.

C *Lowers cholesterol* **B** *Brain support* **V** *Vitamin rich*

REFLAX: SMOOTHIE 5

Makes: approximately 250 ml

YOU NEED

1 tablespoon flaxseed oil • 2 celery sticks • 5 parsley sprigs
½ fennel • 1 handful of green grapes

Add all the ingredients to the blender with 150 ml filtered water. Whizz until
smooth then pour into a plastic sieve set over a jug or bowl. Help the smoothie
through with a rubber spatula or wooden spoon.

This is high in antioxidants, which help prevent diseases.

D *Aids digestion* **D** *Detoxifying* **A** *Anti-inflammatory*

FENNEL SPICED NUT MILK: SMOOTHIE 6

Makes: approximately 300 ml

YOU NEED

30 g almonds • 30 g cashews • 30 g pistachios • 2 Medjool dates, stoned
1 teaspoon fennel seeds • 2 cardamom pods • ½ teaspoon ground cinnamon

---

Add the almonds, cashews, pistachios and dates to the blender with 300 ml filtered
water. Whizz until smooth then pour into a plastic sieve set over a jug or bowl.
Help the smoothie through with a rubber spatula or wooden spoon. Pour into a
saucepan, add the fennel seeds, cardamom pods and cinnamon and
warm gently over a low heat for 3–4 minutes. Sieve again, then serve.

A great milk to increase your iron intake as well as reduce indigestion.

C *Calming*   **B** *Blood building*   **I** *Immunising*

STRESS BUSTER

When we are stressed, we release the hormones adrenaline and cortisol from our adrenal glands at the top of our kidneys. This results in a rise in blood sugar, muscle tension, shallow breathing, higher blood pressure and a rapid heart rate. Also known as the 'fight or flight' response, it can lead to diabetes, weight gain and digestive problems. Luckily we can improve this with diet and lifestyle changes. Eating regularly and sleeping for eight hours a night can help to relax your body. Eating complex carbohydrates and avoiding refined sugar and processed snacks can also be beneficial. Replacing stimulants like alcohol and caffeine with nutrient-dense fuel like green juices can also significantly reduce these symptoms.

Top fruit & vegetables to combat stress

Bananas
Vitamin B6 deficiency has been said to decrease serotonin production, which is one of the key chemicals in your body for improving your mood. Eating bananas daily will keep your serotonin levels up and give you a potassium boost.

Celery
Phthalides, found in the phytonutrients in celery, have a sedative effect, so can help to reduce stress hormones and relax the arterial muscle walls, increasing blood flow. Celery is also an excellent source of vitamins K, C, B6, potassium, folate and fibre.

Swiss chard
Stress can cause you to feel anxious and irritable, and these feelings can be exacerbated by magnesium deficiency. Swiss chard is high in magnesium, which some studies have shown to relieve anxiety.

How many days to detox?
This is a five-day detox plan, but if you haven't detoxed before, I recommend three days for your first try.

Preparation
Shop for all your ingredients two days before. Stock up on extra lemons and herbal teas. Make the smoothies and juices a day before to help you keep to the plan.

Schedule
There are six smoothies to consume each day. In the morning start with a very nutrient-dense smoothie, breaking it up with smoothie 2, the lemon and lime juice (see page 12), and end with a nut milk, which will help prevent you from being hungry in the evening. You don't need to drink your smoothie in one go – you can slowly sip each one if you prefer. I find a wide straw very helpful.

Daily plan:
Repeat this for every day of your detox.

Smoothie 1: 8 a.m.
Smoothie 2: 11 a.m. (see page 12)
Smoothie 3: 1 p.m.
Smoothie 4: 3 p.m.
Smoothie 5: 5 p.m.
Smoothie 6: 7:30 p.m.

You don't need to stick to these times, but allow a two-hour gap before bed. Continue to drink lots of water; I recommend 6–8 glasses a day.

BANANA SPICE: SMOOTHIE 1

Makes: approximately 250 ml

YOU NEED

1 banana, peeled • 200 g natural yoghurt • 1 tablespoon almond butter
1 medjool date, stoned • ½ teaspoon ground cinnamon

—————

Add all the ingredients to the blender with 50 ml filtered water. Whizz until smooth
then pour into a plastic sieve set over a jug or bowl. Help the smoothie through
with a rubber spatula or wooden spoon.

This is high in tryptophan, which the body converts to serotonin, helping to improve your mood.

R *Regulating*   **V** *Vitamin rich*   **MB** *Muscle & bone building*

BUNCH OF CELERY: SMOOTHIE 3

Makes: approximately 300 ml

YOU NEED

2 celery sticks • ½ cucumber

2 handfuls of kale • 1 apple, cored • ½ lemon, peeled • 1 teaspoon honey

---

Add all the ingredients to the blender with 150 ml filtered water. Whizz until smooth then pour into a plastic sieve set over a jug or bowl. Help the smoothie through with a rubber spatula or wooden spoon.

This is great as a post-workout drink, as it replaces your electrolytes and rehydrates the body with rich minerals.

S *Reduces stress* **B** *Blood purifying* **V** *Vitamin rich*

KALE & KIWI: SMOOTHIE 4

Makes: approximately 250 ml

YOU NEED

4 Swiss chard leaves including stems • 2 handfuls of kale
2 celery sticks • 1 kiwi, peeled • 250 ml coconut water

Add all the ingredients to the blender and whizz until smooth then pour into
a plastic sieve set over a jug or bowl. Help the smoothie through
with a rubber spatula or wooden spoon.

A nutrient-rich drink which helps to regulate blood sugar levels.

 Hydrating    Reduces stress    Boosts metabolism

PARSLEY & PINEAPPLE: SMOOTHIE 5

Makes: approximately 400 ml

YOU NEED

⅓ pineapple, peeled and cut into chunks • 2 celery sticks
2 handfuls of spinach • small bunch of parsley

———

Add all the ingredients to the blender with 50 ml filtered water. Whizz until smooth
then pour into a plastic sieve set over a jug or bowl. Help the smoothie through
with a rubber spatula or wooden spoon.

This is full of antioxidants, increasing oxygen levels in the blood.

D *Diuretic* **R** *Revitalising* **B** *Blood purifying*

MANGO NUT MILK: SMOOTHIE 6

Makes: approximately 350 ml

YOU NEED

75 g cashews • 1 mango, peeled and stoned • 1 tablespoon chia seed oil

Add all the ingredients to the blender with 300 ml filtered water. Whizz until smooth then pour into a plastic sieve set over a jug or bowl. Help the milk through with a rubber spatula or wooden spoon. If you feel it is a little thick to drink, try adding more water, or eat it with a spoon.

This nut milk helps alkalise the body and clear the skin.

C *Calming* **V** *Vitamin rich* **I** *Boosts immunity*

PURIFYING

Sometimes your body might feel as though it is running on empty, sluggish in movement or in need of a recharge. A holiday is usually what we crave at times like this, but if one isn't an option, a little health MOT would be beneficial. Taking this purifying detox is a good way to start.

To keep your body healthy, it's important to get rid of any unwanted bacteria or foreign matter lurking in your blood, and expose yourself to as many healthy nutrients as possible. Thankfully smoothies are an easy way to do this.

This detox plan will purify your blood and give your liver a boost.

Top foods to help purify your body

Avocado
High in fibre and good fat, as well as having many vitamins and minerals, avocado also has strong anti-inflammatory properties due to their high variety of carotenoids.

Broccoli
A rich source of essential nutrients, broccoli has many health benefits, including blood purification. It contains anticancer and antioxidant compounds that help the liver to detoxify and clean the blood.

Coriander
This herb is great at detoxifying the body of heavy metals.

Ginger
This spice has a great warming flavour in smoothies. Containing a substance called gingerol, it works to kill parasites or bad bacteria.

How many days to detox?
This is a five-day detox plan, but if you haven't detoxed before, I recommend three days for your first try.

Preparation
Shop for all your ingredients 2 days before. Stock up on extra lemons and herbal teas. Drink ginger tea throughout the day: mix a cup of freshly boiled water with 1 tablespoon grated ginger, a drizzle of honey and a squeeze of lemon. Garlic is a natural antibiotic so take garlic capsules as supplements during the detox. Make the smoothies and juices a day before to help you keep to the plan.

Schedule
There are six smoothies to consume each day. In the morning start with a very nutrient-dense smoothie, breaking it up with smoothie 2, the lemon and lime juice (see page 12), and end with a nut milk. You don't need to drink your smoothie in one go – you can slowly sip them if you prefer. I find a wide straw helpful.

Daily plan:
Repeat this for every day of your detox.

Smoothie 1: 8 a.m.
Smoothie 2: 11 a.m. (see page 12)
Smoothie 3: 1 p.m.
Smoothie 4: 3 p.m.
Smoothie 5: 5 p.m.
Smoothie 6: 7:30 p.m.

You don't need to stick to these times, but allow a two-hour gap before bed. Continue to drink lots of water; I recommend 6–8 glasses a day.

VELVET GREEN: SMOOTHIE 1

Makes: approximately 300 ml

YOU NEED

1 apple, peeled and cored • 1 fennel bulb • ¼ cucumber
1 avocado, peeled and stoned • small handful of green grapes

Add all the ingredients to the blender with 100 ml filtered water. Whizz until
smooth. If you feel it is a little thick, just add more water.

High in iron, this contains nutrients which aid digestion.

M *Mineral rich* **A** *Anti-inflammatory* **D** *Diuretic*

SPROUTING SUCCESS: SMOOTHIE 3

Makes: approximately 250 ml

YOU NEED

2 handfuls of kale • small bunch of parsley • 1 kiwi, peeled
1 lime, peeled • 4 broccoli florets
1 handful of green grapes • ½ teaspoon spirulina powder

Add all the ingredients to the blender with 200 ml filtered water. Whizz until
smooth then pour into a plastic sieve set over a jug or bowl. Help the smoothie
through with a rubber spatula or wooden spoon.

This is high in vitamin C and keeps your liver healthy.

B *Blood purifying* M *Mood enhancing* I *Fights infection*

SWEET ROOTS: SMOOTHIE 4

Makes: approximately 300 ml

YOU NEED

1 carrot • 1 parsnip • 1 medium potato, boiled • 1 lemongrass stalk • 1 apple, cored
1 lime, peeled • 10 coriander sprigs • 1 tablespoon chia seed oil

Add all the ingredients to the blender with 200 ml filtered water. Whizz until
smooth then pour into a plastic sieve set over a jug or bowl. Help the smoothie
through with a rubber spatula or wooden spoon. If you feel it is a little thick, just
add a little more water until it is the consistency you like.

High in folate and potassium, which are great for cardiovascular health.

L *Cleanses liver* **D** *Aids digestion* **A** *Antioxidant rich*

MELON MADNESS: SMOOTHIE 5

Makes: approximately 250 ml

YOU NEED

5 broccoli florets • ¼ small watermelon, peeled

½ cantaloupe, peeled • 1 thumb-sized piece of ginger

Add all the ingredients to the blender. Whizz until smooth then pour into
a plastic sieve set over a jug or bowl. Help the smoothie through
with a rubber spatula or wooden spoon.

Great at reducing inflammation, and keeping your skin
healthy, as it is full of vitamin A.

B *Blood purifying*   **H** *Hydrating*   **VM** *Vitamin & mineral rich*

GINGER MILK NOG: SMOOTHIE 6

Makes: approximately 300 ml

YOU NEED

100 g blanched almonds • 1 thumb-sized piece of ginger • 1 teaspoon honey

———

Add all the ingredients to the blender with 300 ml filtered water. Whizz until smooth then pour into a plastic sieve set over a jug or bowl. Help the milk through with a rubber spatula or wooden spoon.

A milk which naturally boosts your immune system.

C *Calming* **H** *Healing* **MB** *Muscle & bone building*

PROBIOTIC

What you eat and drink has a big impact on your gut, which plays an important role in your overall health. Good bacteria help to fight infection and nourish our bodies by producing vitamins B1, B2, B5, B6 and K and essential fatty acids, antioxidants and amino acids. To keep your gut healthy, you need to feed it with lots of vitamins and minerals – fresh green vegetables are an excellent choice.

Top fruit, vegetables & seeds to help your stomach

Flaxseeds

When these are digested, your intestinal bacteria activate phytoestrogens called lignans. These have been regarded to have anti-cancer and anti-inflammatory properties as well as lowering cholesterol. You can add flaxseed oil to your smoothies.

Natural yoghurt

Live-cultured yoghurts, and particularly homemade yoghurt, are high in probiotics. Be sure to check the label on shop-bought yoghurt as some are high in sugar or full of artificial sweeteners. Goat's milk yoghurt is especially high in probiotics.

Spirulina

This superfood is a microalgae, which when consumed increases the amount of lactobacillus and bifidobacteria in the digestive tract. As an added bonus, it also gives you lots of energy.

How many days to detox?

This is a five-day detox plan, but if you haven't detoxed before, I recommend three days for your first try.

Preparation

Shop for all your ingredients two days before. Stock up on extra lemons and herbal teas. If you can find it, drink kombucha tea, a form of fermented tea, as it contains lots of healthy bacteria. Make the smoothies a day before to help you keep to the plan.

Schedule

There are six smoothies to consume each day. In the morning start with a very nutrient-dense smoothie, breaking it up with smoothie 2, the lemon and lime juice (see page 12), and end with a nut milk, which will help prevent you from being hungry in the evening. You don't need to drink your smoothie in one go – you can slowly sip each one if you prefer. I find a wide straw very helpful.

Daily plan:

Repeat this for every day of your detox.

Smoothie 1: 8 a.m.
Smoothie 2: 11 a.m. (see page 12)
Smoothie 3: 1 p.m.
Smoothie 4: 3 p.m.
Smoothie 5: 5 p.m.
Smoothie 6: 7:30 p.m.

You don't need to stick to these times, but allow a two-hour gap before you go to bed. Continue to drink lots of water; I recommend 6–8 glasses a day.

MORNING YOG: SMOOTHIE 1

Makes: approximately 400 ml

YOU NEED

200 g natural yoghurt • 2 handfuls of blueberries • 8 strawberries, stalks removed

100 ml almond milk • 1 tablespoon oats • 1 tablespoon flaxseed oil

Add all the ingredients to the blender and whizz until smooth.

This tasty smoothie contains a good source of vitamin K, which helps to build blood and strengthen bones.

S *Soothing* **H** *Healing* **D** *Aids digestion*

CLEAN KALE: SMOOTHIE 3

Makes: approximately 350 ml

YOU NEED

½ cos lettuce • ⅓ cucumber • 2 handfuls of blueberries
2 handfuls of kale • 1 apple, cored

Add all the ingredients to the blender with 100 ml filtered water. Whizz until smooth then pour into a plastic sieve set over a jug or bowl. Help the smoothie through with a rubber spatula or wooden spoon.

Full of iron, as well as vitamin C and omega-3 and -6 fatty acids, this is good for your skin health and strengthening your immune system.

P *Purifying* **I** *Fights infection* **B** *Blood building*

TROPICAL TASTE: SMOOTHIE 4

Makes: approximately 250 ml

YOU NEED

1 banana, peeled • ⅓ pineapple, peeled and cut into chunks
2 handfuls of spinach • 150 ml natural yoghurt

———

Add all the ingredients to the blender and whizz until smooth.

Full of lactobacteria and calcium, this helps to protect the colon.

(H) *Hydrating* (B) *Blood purifying* (A) *Antibacterial*

SPIRULINA SMILE: SMOOTHIE 5

Makes: approximately 250 ml

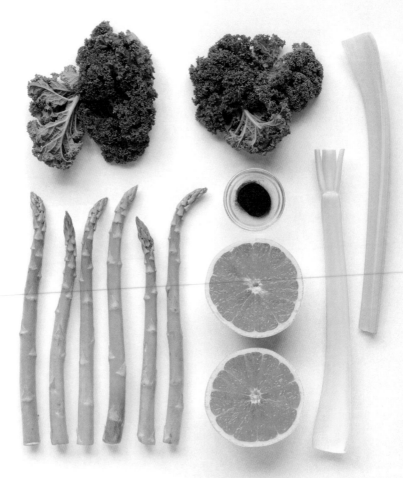

YOU NEED

1 pink grapefruit, peeled • 2 handfuls of kale
6 asparagus spears • 2 celery sticks • 1 teaspoon spirulina powder

---

Add all the ingredients to the blender with 100 ml filtered water. Whizz until
smooth then pour into a plastic sieve set over a jug or bowl. Help the smoothie
through with a rubber spatula or wooden spoon.

A great source of protein and essential nutrients, this smoothie contributes a high percentage of your recommended dietry intake of iron.

B *Blood building*   **P** *Protein rich*   **A** *Alkalising*

GREEN LASSI: SMOOTHIE 6

Makes: approximately 300 ml

YOU NEED

75 g pistachio nuts • 200 g natural yoghurt
1 thumb-sized piece of ginger • 1 Medjool date, stoned • pinch of black pepper

---

Add all the ingredients to the blender with 100 ml filtered water. Whizz until
smooth then pour into a plastic sieve set over a jug or bowl. Help the smoothie
through with a rubber spatula or wooden spoon.

A great milk to aid digestion and soothe the stomach.

C *Calming* **I** *Boosts immunity* **C** *Lowers cholesterol*

ALKALISING

The pH of your blood measures how acid or alkaline your system is. A low pH means that your body is in an acidic state, which can affect your health at a cellular level and encourage fatigue, osteoporosis, candida, muscle loss, kidney stones and, most dramatically, an increase in free radicals. The great news is that eating and drinking alkaline foods, smoothies and juices is the easiest, most efficient way to replenish your cells with alkaline minerals and keep your well-being at an optimum. Alkaline-forming foods include vegetables like lettuce, spinach, kale and spring greens. In theory, the greener the vegetable the more alkaline it is. Fresh fruit and grains like quinoa, amaranth, millet and teff are also good to include in your diet.

Top fruit & vegetables to encourage alkalinity

Lemons
You might think of these yellow fruits as acidic, but once ingested they are actually alkalising. As a natural disinfectant, they can heal wounds and provide potent relief for hyperacidity, virus-related conditions, coughs, colds, flu and heartburn. Lemons also energise the liver and promote detoxification.

Red peppers
Containing essential enzymes for endocrine function, red peppers are one of the best foods for alkalising. They are also known for their antibacterial properties and rich supply of vitamin A, which helps to fight off free radicals that lead to stress and illness.

Roots
As well as being rich in minerals, roots such as beetroot, radishes, parsnips and carrots are good for alkalinity.

How many days to detox?
This is a five-day detox plan, but if you haven't detoxed before, I recommend three days for your first try.

Preparation
Shop for all your ingredients two days before. Stock up on extra lemons and herbal teas. Make the smoothies a day before to help you keep to the plan.

Schedule
There are six smoothies to consume each day. In the morning start with a very nutrient-dense smoothie, breaking it up with smoothie 2, the lemon and lime juice (see page 12), and ending with a nut milk, which will help prevent you from being hungry in the evening. You don't need to drink your smoothie in one go – you can slowly sip each one if you prefer. I find a wide straw to be very helpful.

Daily plan:
Repeat this for every day of your detox.

Smoothie 1: 8 a.m.
Smoothie 2: 11 a.m. (see page 12)
Smoothie 3: 1 p.m.
Smoothie 4: 3 p.m.
Smoothie 5: 5 p.m.
Smoothie 6: 7:30 p.m.

You don't need to stick to these times, but allow a two-hour gap before bed. Continue to drink lots of water; I recommend 6–8 glasses a day.

GREEN IN LINE: SMOOTHIE 1

Makes: approximately 300 ml

YOU NEED

2 handfuls of kale • handful of baby spinach
¼ cucumber • handful of green grapes • 1 kiwi, peeled

Add all the ingredients to the blender with 100 ml filtered water. Whizz until
smooth then pour into a plastic sieve over a jug or bowl. Help the smoothie through
with a rubber spatula or wooden spoon.

High in vitamin C, this smoothie is a great immune booster.

L *Cleanses liver* **M** *Mineral rich* **ME** *Mood enhancing*

MORNING FRESH: SMOOTHIE 3

Makes: approximately 300 ml

YOU NEED

½ cos lettuce • 1 lemon, peeled • ½ white cabbage
1 orange, peeled • 10 mint leaves

Add all the ingredients to the blender with 100 ml filtered water. Whizz until smooth then pour into a plastic sieve set over a jug or bowl. Help the smoothie through with a rubber spatula or wooden spoon.

The vitamin C, folate and potassium in this smoothie keep your blood sugar levels on an even keel.

A *Alkalising* **D** *Aids digestion* **V** *Vitamin rich*

PURPLE SUNSHINE: SMOOTHIE 4

Makes: approximately 350 ml

YOU NEED

¼ red cabbage (about 125 g) • 2 celery sticks
4 plums, stoned • large handful of blackberries

Add all the ingredients to the blender with 100 ml filtered water. Whizz until smooth then pour into a plastic sieve set over a jug or bowl. Help the smoothie through with a rubber spatula or wooden spoon.

Full of powerful vitamins to keep your immune system healthy.

L *Cleanses liver* **D** *Detoxifying* **C** *Deep cleansing*

ENERGISING PEPPER: SMOOTHIE 5

Makes: approximately 250 ml

YOU NEED

2 beetroots • 1 red pepper, deseeded • handful of kale

1 apple, cored • 1 teaspoon barley grass powder

Add all the ingredients to the blender with 200 ml filtered water. Whizz until smooth then pour into a plastic sieve set over a jug or bowl. Help the smoothie through with a rubber spatula or wooden spoon.

This is bursting with vitamins A, C and K, to support your immune function and reduce inflammation.

 *Anti-inflammatory*  *Cleansing*  *Vitamin rich*

BRAZILIAN BEDTIME: SMOOTHIE 6

Makes: approximately 300 ml

YOU NEED

100 g Brazil nuts • 5 Medjool dates • pinch of salt • 2 drops of vanilla extract

---

Add all the ingredients to the blender with 300 ml filtered water. Whizz until smooth then pour into a plastic sieve set over a jug or bowl. Help the juice through with a rubber spatula or wooden spoon.

This nut milk contains selenium, which is an essential trace mineral for the immune system and thyroid function.

M *Mineral rich*　**C** *Calming*　**A** *Antioxidant*

SUMMER BOOSTER

This detox is an all-rounder, and doesn't concentrate on just one element of the body. If you want to feel refreshed, revitalised and ready to get out there in the sunshine, this plan will give you the boost you need. Sometimes the winter leaves you feeling a little tired, with the urge to feel healthy. This plan will give you confidence, help you to feel better from within and give a boost to your skin.

Top fruit & vegetables that are full of boosting nutrients

Cantaloupe
Rich in vitamin C and potassium, the cantaloupe is a delicious, juicy fruit with many health benefits.

Kale
This cruciferous vegetable is king when it comes to fibre. It keeps you full for a long time, contains antioxidants, is high in omega 3 and even has anti-inflammatory qualities.

Raspberries
These delicious berries are great in smoothies, and still just as nutrient-rich if used from frozen. They contain high levels of vitamins and minerals including potassium, calcium and folate, which help to maintain good blood pressure as well as promote bone development and growth.

How many days to detox?
This is a five-day detox plan, but if you haven't detoxed before, I recommend three days for your first try.

Preparation
Shop for all your ingredients two days before. Stock up on extra lemons and herbal teas. Make the smoothies and juices a day before to help you keep to the plan.

Schedule
There are six smoothies to consume each day. In the morning start with a very nutrient-dense smoothie, breaking it up with smoothie 2, the lemon and lime juice (see page 12), and end with a nut milk, which will help prevent you from being hungry in the evening. You don't need to drink your smoothie in one go – you can happily sip each one if you prefer. I find a wide straw to be very helpful.

Daily plan:
Repeat this for every day of your detox.

Smoothie 1: 8 a.m.
Smoothie 2: 11 a.m. (see page 12)
Smoothie 3: 1 p.m.
Smoothie 4: 3 p.m.
Smoothie 5: 5 p.m.
Smoothie 6: 7:30 p.m.

You don't need to stick to these times, but allow a two-hour gap before bed. Continue to drink lots of water; I recommend 6–8 glasses a day.

KALE ROOT: SMOOTHIE 1

Makes: approximately 300 ml

YOU NEED

2 handfuls of kale • 2 small beetroot, chopped
1 orange, peeled • small bunch of parsley • 2 celery sticks
½ lemon, peeled • 1 tablespoon flaxseed oil

Add all the ingredients to the blender with 200 ml filtered water. Whizz until
smooth then pour into a plastic sieve set over a jug or bowl. Help the smoothie
through with a rubber spatula or wooden spoon.

This smoothie is high in calcium, which is good for your bones.

A *Anti-inflammatory* **D** *Aids digestion* **A** *Antixoxidant*

SPICED BERRIES: SMOOTHIE 3

Makes: approximately 300 ml

YOU NEED

2 handfuls of watercress • 2 large handfuls of red grapes
2 handfuls of raspberries (about 150 g) • 1 thumb-sized piece of ginger

---

Add all the ingredients to the blender with 200 ml filtered water. Whizz until
smooth then pour into a plastic sieve set over a jug or bowl. Help the smoothie
through with a rubber spatula or wooden spoon.

Highly nutritious, this is packed with vitamins A, B, C and E,
beta-carotene, folate and calcium.

B *Blood building* **VM** *Vitamin & mineral rich* **D** *Aids digestion*

SUMMER MINT: SMOOTHIE 4

Makes: approximately 300 ml

YOU NEED

¼ cucumber • ½ cantaloupe melon, peeled
2 handfuls of strawberries, stalks removed • 5 mint leaves

Add all the ingredients to the blender with 50 ml filtered water. Whizz until smooth
then pour into a plastic sieve set over a jug or bowl. Help the smoothie through with
a rubber spatula or wooden spoon.

A well-rounded smoothie, good for a healthy immune system.

V *Vitamin rich* **H** *Hydrating* **R** *Revitalising*

CALM COMPLEXION: SMOOTHIE 5

Makes: approximately 400 ml

YOU NEED

1 apple, peeled and cored • 2 handfuls of kale

½ large avocado, peeled • ¼ cucumber

Add all the ingredients to the blender with 200 ml filtered water. The avocado makes this smoothie quite thick. If you want to thin it, try adding a little water; otherwise eat with a spoon.

This is full of healthy monounsaturated fat that is
essential for plump, youthful skin.

S *Improves skin*   **A** *Anti-inflammatory*   **P** *Purifying*

SLEEPY SPICE: SMOOTHIE 6

Makes: approximately 300 ml

YOU NEED

75 g blanched almonds • pinch of saffron threads

pinch of ground cardamom or 2 pods, seeds removed and ground

2 Medjool dates, stoned

Add all the ingredients to the blender with 300 ml filtered water. Whizz until
smooth then pour into a plastic sieve set over a jug or bowl. Help the milk through
with a rubber spatula or wooden spoon.

This nut milk will lift your mood, support your eyesight and improve your memory.

C *Calming* **H** *Healing* **A** *Antibacterial*

IMMUNITY BOOSTER

A nutritious diet is very important, not only for your immune system but also for bone health. Sometimes after having a cold or coming down with an infection, it takes a while to feel back to normal. Try this detox to kickstart your immune system and give you what you need to feel like yourself again.

Top fruit & vegetables to help boost your immune system

Acai berries
Commonly found in dried form, the acai berry is very dark in colour signifying that it is high in antioxidants, which studies have suggested help you maintain immune health as you age.

Cabbages
Cabbage is high in amino acids and is believed to help those who are suffering from inflammation. It is also an excellent source of vitamins C and K. Vitamin K is antibacterial and strengthens your immune system.

Watermelons
This colourful melon is refreshing, hydrating and packed with powerful antioxidants. Glutathione is found in the red pulpy flesh near the rind, which helps fight infection and strengthen your immune system.

How many days to detox?
This is a five-day detox plan, but if you haven't detoxed before, I recommend three days for your first try.

Preparation
Shop for all your ingredients two days before. Stock up on extra lemons and herbal teas. Make the smoothies and juices a day before to help you keep to the plan.

Schedule
There are six smoothies to consume each day. In the morning start with a very nutrient-dense smoothie, breaking it up with smoothie 2, the lemon and lime juice (see page 12), and end with a nut milk, which will help prevent you from being hungry in the evening. You don't need to drink your smoothie in one go – you can slowly sip each one if you prefer. I find a wide straw to be very helpful.

Daily plan:
Repeat this for every day of your detox.

Smoothie 1: 8 a.m.
Smoothie 2: 11 a.m. (see page 12)
Smoothie 3: 1 p.m.
Smoothie 4: 3 p.m.
Smoothie 5: 5 p.m.
Smoothie 6: 7:30 p.m.

You don't need to stick to these times, but allow a two-hour gap before bed. Continue to drink lots of water; I recommend 6–8 glasses a day.

COCO MELON: SMOOTHIE 1

Makes: approximately 300 ml

YOU NEED
100 ml almond milk • ¼ small watermelon, peeled
100 g raw coconut • 100 ml natural yoghurt • 1 teaspoon honey

---

Add all the ingredients to the blender and whizz until smooth then pour
into a plastic sieve set over a jug or bowl. Help the smoothie through
with a rubber spatula or wooden spoon.

An excellent smoothie for killing harmful bacteria and viruses.

H *Hydrating*　**B** *Blood purifying*　**R** *Revitalising*

SAVOY BERRY: SMOOTHIE 3

Makes: approximately 300 ml

YOU NEED

10 strawberries, stalks removed • 200 g Savoy cabbage
1 lime, peeled • 1 small bunch of mint

Add all the ingredients to the blender with 200 ml filtered water. Whizz until smooth then pour into a plastic sieve set over a jug or bowl. Help the smoothie through with a rubber spatula or wooden spoon.

This is full of potent antioxidants and vitamins A, C, E and K.

(I) *Boosts immunity* (H) *Healing* (I) *Fights infection*

RED VEG: SMOOTHIE 4

Makes: approximately 300 ml

YOU NEED

¼ cucumber • 2 small carrots • 1 celery stick • ¼ red cabbage (120 g)

1 lemon, peeled • 1 thumb-sized piece of ginger • small bunch of red grapes

---

Add all the ingredients to the blender with 200 ml filtered water. Whizz until smooth then pour into a plastic sieve set over a jug or bowl. Help the smoothie through with a rubber spatula or wooden spoon.

This smoothie is high in vitamin A, which helps with eyesight.

M *Boosts metabolism* **D** *Aids digestion* **A** *Antibacterial*

ACAI WATER: SMOOTHIE 5

Makes: approximately 300 ml

YOU NEED

¼ watermelon, peeled • ½ cucumber

1 small bunch of coriander • 1 teaspoon acai powder

Add all the ingredients to the blender with 100 ml filtered water. Whizz until smooth then pour into a plastic sieve set over a jug or bowl. Help the smoothie through with a rubber spatula or wooden spoon.

Full of essential fatty acids, this will set you on a path of good health.

H *Hydrating* **V** *Vitamin rich* **B** *Blood building*

CHOC BRAZIL NUT: SMOOTHIE 6

Makes: approximately 300 ml

YOU NEED

75 g Brazil nuts • 1 tablespoon coconut oil

1 Medjool date, stoned • 1 teaspoon raw cacao nibs

Add all the ingredients to the blender with 300 ml filtered water. Whizz until smooth then pour into a plastic sieve set over a jug or bowl. Help the milk through with a rubber spatula or wooden spoon.

Full of magnesium, which helps to relax muscles, improves peristalsis in the bowels and relaxes the heart and cardiovascular system.

B *Stabilises blood sugar*   **R** *Relaxing*   **A** *Anti-inflammatory*

WEIGHT LOSS DETOX

If you feel that you have been overeating and perhaps not exercising as much as you would like, then try this detox to lose a few pounds Consuming too many fatty foods and increasing your blood sugar level can cause cravings, irritability and mood swings. To avoid this, make sure you get regular exercise, which improves your mood. Stay hydrated, and when the detox is over continue drinking a smoothie as a snack as part of your daily routine.

Top fruit & vegetables to help keep cravings at bay

Avocado
Avocados are great to keep your blood sugar stable. They can't be juiced but are perfect for shakes and smoothies. Although they are high in calories, they are full of good fats.

Grapefruit
Grapefruit contains phytochemicals, which suppress appetite. It is full of vitamin C and can stimulate your metabolism, which helps burn fat.

Broccoli
Broccoli is low in calories and sugar, and can be added to any smoothie. Broccoli contains compounds that help drive blood sugar into the cell walls quickly. It is also suppresses appetite.

How many days to detox?
If you have never detoxed before, then you may want to start with a three-day plan. If you regularly drink green juices, have detoxed before or eat a lot of raw food, then this detox can last five days.

Preparation
Shop for all your ingredients two days before. Stock up on extra lemons and herbal teas to help with your detox. Make the smoothies and juices a day before to help you keep to the plan.

Schedule
There are six smoothies to consume each day. In the morning start with a very nutrient-dense smoothie, breaking it up with smoothie 2, the lemon and lime juice (see page 12), and end with a nut milk, which will help prevent you from being hungry in the evening. You don't need to drink your smoothie in one go – you can slowly sip each one if you prefer. I find a wide straw helpful.

Daily plan:
Repeat this for every day of your detox.

Smoothie 1: 8 a.m.
Smoothie 2: 11 a.m. (see page 12)
Smoothie 3: 1 p.m.
Smoothie 4: 3 p.m.
Smoothie 5: 5 p.m.
Smoothie 6: 7:30 p.m.

You don't need to stick to these times, but allow a two-hour gap before bed. Drink water throughout the day and, if you feel like drinking tea, try herbal or green tea.

MORNING GRAPEFRUIT: SMOOTHIE 1

Makes: approximately 300 ml

YOU NEED

1 grapefruit, peeled • 1 apple, cored and chopped
2 handfuls of kale • 5 mint leaves

Put all the ingredients into the blender with 100 ml filtered water. Whizz until
smooth then pour into a plastic sieve set over a jug or bowl. Help the smoothie
through with a rubber spatula or wooden spoon.

This is bursting with vitamin C, contributing to a healthy immune system.

H *Suppresses hunger* **V** *Vitamin rich* **D** *Aids digestion*

AVOCADO FEAST: SMOOTHIE 3

Makes: approximately 500 ml (2 servings)

YOU NEED

1 avocado, stoned and peeled • juice of ½ lime • 2 parsley sprigs
5 mint leaves • ½ cucumber • handful of seedless green grapes

---

This smoothie makes enough for 2 days. Add all the ingredients to the blender
with 300 ml filtered water. Whizz until smooth.

This delicious smoothie is rich in vitamins B, C, E and K.

B *Stabilises blood sugar* **P** *Protein rich* **S** *Strengthening*

BRILLIANT BROCCOLI: SMOOTHIE 4

Makes: approximately 300 ml

YOU NEED

4 broccoli florets • ¼ baby watermelon (about 250 g), peeled

3 radishes • 100 ml coconut water

———

Add all the ingredients to the blender and whizz until smooth, then pour
into a plastic sieve set over a jug or bowl. Help the smoothie through
with a rubber spatula or wooden spoon.

Bursting with vitamins, this will help to improve your cardiovascular system.

H *Supresses hunger* **A** *Antibacterial* **B** *Blood building*

SPIRULINA SHAKE: SMOOTHIE 5

Makes: approximately 400 ml

YOU NEED

1 teaspoon spirulina powder • 2 handfuls of spinach • 1 apple, cored

½ cucumber • 4 parsley sprigs

———

Add all the ingredients to the blender with 100 ml filtered water. Whizz until
smooth then pour into a plastic sieve set over a jug or bowl. Help the smoothie
through with a rubber spatula or wooden spoon.

This is highly nutritious and particularly good for brain function.

B *Stabilises blood sugar* **P** *Protein rich* **V** *Vitamin rich*

CINNAMON & CASHEW MILK: SMOOTHIE 6

Makes: approximately 320 ml

YOU NEED

100 g cashews • 1 teaspoon ground cinnamon

2 Medjool dates • 1 teaspoon agave nectar

Add all the ingredients to a blender with 300 ml filtered water. Whizz until smooth
then pour into a plastic sieve set over a jug or bowl. Help the milk through
with a rubber spatula or wooden spoon.

This smoothie is packed with antioxidants and is a great anti-inflammatory.

 *Antioxidant*  *Calming*  *Healing*

JANUARY DETOX

After burning the candle at both ends and over-indulging on all things delicious, you might feel that your body is craving some tender loving care. Often after the festive season we feel even more tired, our skin is puffy and our waistlines might have expanded slightly. This plan is a great way to start the year and to get your body reinvigorated, feeling full of energy and raring to go.

Top fruit & vegetables to help with all-round health

Beetroot
This is a great vegetable for juices and smoothies as it is a natural sweetener. Full of folic acid, potassium, magnesium, iron as well as vitamins, A, B6, and C, beetroot naturally boosts your stamina.

Blueberries
This little North American fruit packs a powerful nutritional punch. Full of vitamins C and K, blueberries help boost your immune system.

Chia seeds
These black seeds (which you can also buy as an oil) are native to Mexico and Guatemala. They are packed full of nutrients, which can have an important effect on the body and brain. Loaded with antioxidants, full of protein and high in omega-3 fatty acids, it's no wonder these seeds are becoming popular. Chia seed oil can be found online, and is a great way to add chia to a smoothie.

How many days to detox?
This is a five-day detox plan, but if you haven't detoxed before, I recommend three days for your first try.

Preparation
Shop for all your ingredients two days before. Stock up on extra lemons and herbal teas. Make the smoothies and juices a day before to help you keep to the plan.

Schedule
There are six smoothies to consume each day. In the morning start with a very nutrient-dense smoothie, breaking it up with smoothie 2, the lemon and lime juice (see page 12), and end with a nut milk, which will help prevent you from being hungry in the evening. You don't need to drink your smoothie in one go – you can slowly sip each one if you prefer. I find a wide straw very helpful.

Daily plan:
Repeat this for every day of your detox.

Smoothie 1: 8 a.m.
Smoothie 2: 11 a.m. (see page 12)
Smoothie 3: 1 p.m.
Smoothie 4: 3 p.m.
Smoothie 5: 5 p.m.
Smoothie 6: 7:30 p.m.

You don't need to stick to these times, but allow a two-hour gap before bed. Continue to drink lots of water, I recommend 6–8 glasses a day.

CHIA WAKE UP: SMOOTHIE 1

Makes: approximately 350 ml

YOU NEED

3 handfuls of blueberries • 1 orange, peeled • 2 small carrots
4 broccoli florets • 1 tablespoon chia seed oil

Add all the ingredients to the blender with 150 ml filtered water. Whizz until smooth then pour into a plastic sieve set over a jug or bowl. Help the smoothie through with a rubber spatula or wooden spoon.

This smoothie is full of omega-3 fatty acids, which help to reduce inflammation.

E *Energising* **D** *Aids digestion* **B** *Stabilises blood sugar*

SPINACH BOOST: SMOOTHIE 3

Makes: approximately 250 ml

YOU NEED
1 celery stick • 2 handfuls of baby spinach
1 small bunch of parsley • ⅓ pineapple, cut into chunks

Add all the ingredients to the blender with 100 ml filtered water. Whizz until smooth then pour into a plastic sieve set over a jug or bowl. Help the smoothie through with a rubber spatula or wooden spoon.

Full of antioxidants, this smoothie will give you a health boost.

V *Vitamin rich*   **R** *Revitalising*   **A** *Anti-inflammatory*

ENERGY BEETROOT: SMOOTHIE 4

Makes: approximately 250 ml

YOU NEED

1 apple, cored • 1 carrot • 2 small beetroot
small bunch of mint • 1 lemon, peeled • 1 thumb-sized piece of ginger

---

Add all the ingredients to the blender with 150 ml filtered water. Whizz until
smooth then pour into a plastic sieve set over a jug or bowl. Help the smoothie
through with a rubber spatula or wooden spoon.

A great liver cleanser to help eliminate toxins from the blood.

M *Mineral rich* **S** *Stamina boosting* **B** *Blood purifying*

BLUE MOON: SMOOTHIE 5

Makes: approximately 350 ml

YOU NEED

3 handfuls of blueberries • 1 orange, peeled
3 handfuls of kale • ½ cucumber • 1 teaspoon spirulina powder

---

Add all the ingredients to the blender with 150 ml filtered water. Whizz until smooth then pour into a plastic sieve set over a jug or bowl. Help the smoothie through with a rubber spatula or wooden spoon.

This smoothie is full of antioxidants to keep your heart healthy.

I *Boosts immunity*   **S** *Strengthening*   **P** *Purifying*

ALMOND VANILLA: SMOOTHIE 6

Makes: approximately 300 ml

YOU NEED

100 g almonds • 2 drops vanilla extract • 2 Medjool dates
1 tablespoon chia seed oil

Add all the ingredients to the blender with 300 ml filtered water. Whizz until
smooth then pour into a plastic sieve set over a jug or bowl. Help the milk through
with a rubber spatula or wooden spoon.

A nourishing nut milk to help to regulate your blood sugar.

C *Calming* **H** *Healing* **D** *Aids digestion*

INDEX

Acknowledgements
I would like to thank everyone who worked on *Super Smoothies* along with
Marabout, Catie Ziller, Kathy Steer and Alice Chadwick. Also a big thank you to
Deirdre Rooney for your lovely photos as always. Thanks to Poppy Campbell and
Louisa Chapman-Andrews for whizzing the machine incessantly on the shoot.
And finally, a big thanks to my detox testers, you have been brilliant.

Super Smoothies by Fern Green

First published in 2015 by Hachette Books
(Marabout)
This English hardback edition published in 2017
by Hardie Grant Books

Hardie Grant Books (UK)
52-54 Southwark Street
London SE1 1UN
hardiegrant.co.uk

Hardie Grant Books (Australia)
Ground Floor, Building 1
658 Church Street
Melbourne, VIC 3121
hardiegrant.com.au

British Library Cataloguing-in-Publication Data.
A catalogue record for this book is available
from the British Library.

ISBN: 978-1-78488-105-4

Publisher: Catie Ziller
Editor: Kathy Steer
Designer & illustrator: Alice Chadwick
Author: Fern Green
Photographer: Deirdre Rooney

For the English hardback edition:
Publisher: Kate Pollard
Senior Editor: Kajal Mistry
Editorial Assistant: Hannah Roberts
Proofreader: Jessica Gooch
Colour Reproduction by p2d

Printed and bound in China by 1010

10 9 8 7 6 5 4 3 2 1